MIKE YOU

SUPERTED
AND THE TRAIN ROBBERS

*Illustrations by Chris Fenna
and Mike Wall*

Frederick Muller Limited
London

A thick blanket of snow covers the mountains and trees in the French Alps. A steam train is making its way through the mountains carrying a lovely big load of chocolate. It hurries along the narrow winding track beneath a snowy crag, where two figures are standing . . . train robbers.

"O.K. Bulk, when I give the signal, you blow the horn."

"What tune would you like Tex?"

"Just blow, idiot."

"Sure, Tex, why?"

Texas Pete impatiently explains.

"You blow the horn. Skeleton's down the track, he hears the horn and changes the points, the train goes into the siding, it stops, we get in and drive it away. Get the picture?"

Bulk is a little puzzled. "What picture, Tex? I can't see any picture."

"Forget it," yells Texas Pete. "Here comes the train. Ready? Then blow."

Bulk puffs out his cheeks and blows into the air.

Texas Pete grabs him by his braces and menacingly growls, "The horn you idiot."

Bulk blasts the horn. The sound starts an avalanche. Bulk is swept down the mountainside, and falls onto the railway points diverting the train into a tunnel. There is a squealing of brakes.

Not far away, our two heroes are waiting for a train. Spottyman, Ted's special friend from the planet Spot, is getting very impatient. "Oh, I do wish that train would hurry up. Why do we have to go by train anyway, it's quicker by rocket."

Ted smiles kindly. "But we're on holiday, Spotty. It would be a waste of rocket fuel. I am beginning to get worried, I think there might have been an accident. Let's take a look."

Spotty jumps up excitedly. Could this be the start of another adventure? "I've got my rocket-pack here."

"No Spotty, we came for a skiing holiday and I want to ski. Besides, you need the practice."

Spottyman reluctantly collects his skis and wishes he was back on the planet Spot.

Texas Pete, Bulk and Skeleton, walk through a snowdrift towards the tunnel and the stranded train. Only Tex has snow shoes on. Poor Bulk and Skeleton slowly sink into the snow. As usual, Skeleton is complaining.

"Oh no, not more cold wet snow, I'll get rheumatism, I know I will."

They reach the tunnel and Tex spots the end of the train. The avalanche has caused a snowdrift to block the other end of the tunnel. "Hey, the train's still in there. Let's go!"

Not far away Ted and Spotty are skiing across the mountains. Spotty is not a good skier.

Ted calls, "Hurry up, Spotty."

"B.b.b.but I've never skied before. You see, we d.d.d.don't have snow on Spot."

The pals can't see that the slope ends with a small cliff. Ted soars over the cliff in classic ski-jump style. "It's almost like flying," he yells.

Spotty hurtles head over heels and crashes. Ted asks anxiously, "Spotty! Are you all right?"

"Oh, oh, oh, SuperTed, I've got stripes in front of my eyes."

Ted can see Spotty's just a bit winded and laughs. "Stripes! That'll make a change."

He helps his friend to his feet. "Come on, Spotty. Bubbling blancmange! Look, footprints. I get the feeling that there's something going on here that I don't like."

Meanwhile, deep in the tunnel the train robbers make their way towards the train. Skeleton is worried, "Tex, it's dark, it's cold, the roof's simply dripping with water, there are probably bats . . ."

Suddenly they see a shadow. Worried they move stealthily towards it.

A young train driver steps from behind the hissing engine. "Oh, hello," she says "I'm having a little trouble. Would you mind helping me clear the snow?"

Bulk, always the gentleman, steps forward. "What? Help? Oh yeah, love to."

Skeleton is used to being told what to do and also offers to help. "I don't mind. I'm game for anything."

Texas Pete is furious. "Grab her you dummies!"

The girl screams.

Ted and Spottyman have followed the footprints straight into the dark tunnel. Ted is a bit nervous. "Stick close to me Spotty, there's something moving in there."

Suddenly the train comes speeding round a bend in the tunnel, towards them. The bright headlights are dazzling. Spottyman is crushed to the wall of the tunnel. Ted disappears under the wheels of the train. Luckily, he is untouched by the wagons, as they pass over him.

"Pulsating prunes! Spotty. Where are you Spotty?"

A groan comes from the direction of the wall as Spottyman dusts himself down. "I think you ought to say your magic word SuperTed."

Ted agrees. "And you should switch on your rocket-pack. If we ski after those train robbers we'll never catch them."

Aboard the speeding train, Texas Pete orders Bulk to work harder. "Come on, Bulk. Faster . . . shovel more coal onto that fire."

"Anything you say Tex."

Above them SuperTed and Spottyman are flying at full speed. "It's going too fast SuperTed. Even if we catch it, we'll never be able to land."

SuperTed is determined. "We've got to try Spotty. I'll head for the guard's van and you land on one of the carriages."

As they land on the train, it enters another tunnel and Spottyman is knocked off the train into the snow by the top of the tunnel.

SuperTed is flat against the roof of the wagons crawling towards the engine. He is coughing and blinded by the smoke.

He crawls forward and can see Tex standing at the controls. "Stop that train Texas Pete."

"Heh! Heh! Heh! Having fun, SuperTed? It's just a little train robbery, nothing to get steamed up about. Hey Bulk."

"Yeah Tex."

"Disconnect the carriages. We'll leave that puny teddy miles behind."

Bulk's brain grinds into action. "Now if I lean over here, like this, and pull that lever . . ." He disconnects the carriage, but forgets to let go. "Hang on, what's this . . ? Help!" Bulk's feet are caught at the back of the engine and his body begins to stretch.

SuperTed climbs down off the wagon and using Bulk as a footbridge steps onto the engine.

Tex goes for his guns. "Why, I'll blast you out of existence."

SuperTed dives forward, and with his rocket boots at full power, shouts, "No you don't. Feel like a spin, Tex?" He twirls the cowboy around until he's tied up in his own lasso.

The young train driver shouts a warning. "Quick, SuperTed, put the brake on."

With one long reverse blast of his rocket boots SuperTed brings the train to a screeching halt.

The jerk squashes Bulk back into his normal round shape. He loses his balance. Bulk and Skeleton, who has been hiding in one of the wagons, are both thrown out of the train and into a snowdrift.

Much later SuperTed and Spottyman are enjoying their skiing holiday.

As he whizzes along, SuperTed shouts, "Well, your skiing has improved Spotty."

Spotty is pleased. "Yes, it's easy when you know how."

With that, Spotty flops down into the snow, and SuperTed just cannot stop laughing.